GLEN ROY

A LANDSCAPE FASHIONED BY GEOLOGY

©Scottish Natural Heritage 2004

ISBN 1 85397 360 2

A CIP record is held at the British Library

NP3K0204

Acknowledgements

Authors: Douglas Peacock, John Gordon and Frank May

Series editor: Alan McKirdy (SNH)

Text on pages 28, 29: Alison Grant

Photography:

National Oceanic & Atmospheric Administration 22 left;

Julia Margaret Cameron/National Portrait Gallery, London 22 centre;

Lorne Gill/SNH front cover, back cover, frontispiece, 6, 16 bottom, 18, 21 top, 21 bottom, 23, 24, 25, 27, 28; **John Gordon** 7, 8, 11, 14, 15, 19 top, 19 bottom ; **P&A MacDonald/SNH** 4, 10, 16 top, 20, 26 left, 26 right; **Andrew Russell/University of Keele** 12; **University of Aberdeen** 22 right.

Illustrations:

Craig Ellery 2, 3, 9, 17, 27; **Iain McIntosh** contents page.

Further copies of this book and other publications can be obtained from:

The Publications Section,

Scottish Natural Heritage,

Battleby, Redgorton, Perth PH1 3EW

Tel: 01738 444177 Fax: 01738 827411

E-mail: pubs@snh.gov.uk

www.snh.org.uk

Front cover image:
view of the Brunachan fan, Glen Roy
Back cover image:
classic view of the Glen Roy National
Nature Reserve from the car park view point

GLEN ROY

A Landscape Fashioned by Geology

by

Douglas Peacock, John Gordon and Frank May

Modern glacier and ice-dammed lake: Moreno Glacier, Argentina (from a photo by J.E. Gordon)

Contents

Travellers and local people alike have long been fascinated by the Parallel Roads of Lochaber. Were these striking horizontal lines on the hillsides of Glen Roy, Glen Gloy and Glen Spean formed by giants of old, as described in Gaelic myths? Are they natural or were they formed by human activity? In the 19th century, the Parallel Roads attracted the attention of many of the founding fathers of modern geology, including the Reverend William Buckland, James Geikie, Charles Darwin, Charles Lyell and Joseph Prestwich. This interest ensured that the Parallel Roads, and Glen Roy in particular, featured prominently in the development of geological science.

Interest in the Parallel Roads continues to this day, both among earth scientists intrigued by the dramatic geological and geomorphological processes that shaped the landscape, and among modern travellers and tourists attracted by the natural wonder of the landforms. This booklet traces the story of the formation of the Parallel Roads - a remarkable story of ice-age glaciers, vast lakes and catastrophic floods.

The Glen Roy Area Through Time

QUATERNARY **THE "ICE AGE"** 2.4 million years ago up to and including recent times 		**Present day to 1,500 years ago.** Increased land improvements and forest clearance. Enhanced slope erosion and gully formation. **6,000 years ago.** Start of significant woodland clearance by human activity. **10,000 years ago.** Establishment of woodland. **11,500 years ago.** Climate warms very rapidly. Glaciers melt and ice-dammed lakes in Glen Roy, Glen Gloy and Spean drain for the last time. Landslides and rockfalls occur due to stress release and ground thawing. **12,500 years ago.** Climate becomes extremely cold again at the start of Loch Lomond Stadial. An icefield forms in the West Highlands. Glaciers from this icefield block the drainage in Glen Roy, Glen Goy and Glean Spean, allowing formation of ice-dammed lakes and the Parallel Roads. **14,700 years ago.** Climate warms rapidly, with summer temperatures comparable to those of today. Glaciers retreat rapidly. **22,000 years ago.** A vast sheet of ice covers all but a few mountain tops and extends at least 100km west of the Scottish mainland. **29,000 years ago.** Climate cools and the last major ice sheet glaciation (Late Devensian) begins. **2.4 million to 29,000 years ago.** Many glacial episodes with short warmer (interglacial) intervals. Erosion by ice sheets and mountain glaciers.
NEOGENE 2.4 to 24 million years		Tropical conditions are widespread, although the climate cools as the Ice Age approaches.
PALEOGENE 24 to 65 million years		The North Atlantic Ocean continues to widen. Active volcanoes on Skye, Mull and Rum pour out great volumes of lava.
CRETACEOUS 65 to 142 million years		Sea levels are higher than today. Warm, shallow, temperate seas fringe the low-lying land, with chalk deposited across Scotland, but later removed by erosion.
JURASSIC 142 to 206 million years	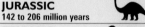	Opening of the North Atlantic Ocean begins. Climate is warm and humid. Sea levels are considerably higher than today.
TRIASSIC 206 to 248 million years		Scotland is located in near-equatorial latitudes, in a similar position to sub-Saharan Africa today, and desert conditions are widespread.
PERMIAN 248 to 290 million years		Desert conditions prevail across Scotland. Violent earthquakes rock the land.
CARBONIFEROUS 290 to 354 million years		Scotland sits astride the equator.
DEVONIAN 354 to 417 million years		The high mountains created by the colliding continents are rapidly eroded and debris carried to lower ground by streams and rivers. Movements on the Great Glen Fault produce a zone of broken rock. The Ben Nevis volcano is active!
SILURIAN 417 to 443 million years		The earth continues to move as Scotland collides with Baltica (Norway and Sweden) and Avalonia (England). A mountain chain (the Caledonian Mountain Belt) as high as the Himalayas is created as a result of these collisions.
ORDOVICIAN 443 to 490 million years		The ancient sands and muds, laid down in Precambrian times, are cooked and squashed as they become deeply buried within the earth's crust.
CAMBRIAN 490 to 545 million years		Scotland moves north from a position close to the South Pole!
PRECAMBRIAN 545 to 3,500 million years		Great thicknesses of sands and muds are deposited. These are later altered to form the bedrock of the Glen Roy area.

Map of the Bedrock in the Glen Roy Area

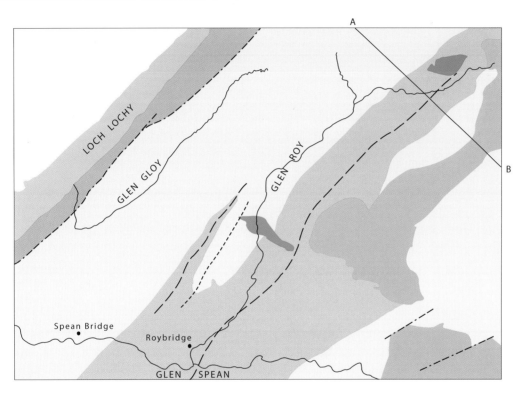

A
B

LOCH LOCHY

GLEN GLOY

GLEN ROY

Spean Bridge

Roybridge

GLEN SPEAN

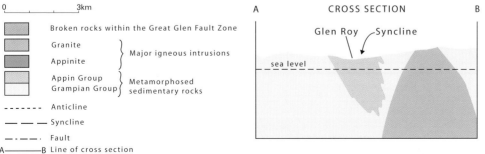

0   3km

Broken rocks within the Great Glen Fault Zone

Granite
Appinite   } Major igneous intrusions

Appin Group
Grampian Group   } Metamorphosed sedimentary rocks

- - - - - - - Anticline

— — — Syncline

—·—·— Fault

A————B Line of cross section

A   CROSS SECTION   B

Glen Roy   Syncline

sea level

The cross section (line A - B on the map above) shows some of the intense folding and compression that has occurred in the rocks that were originally laid down in horizontal beds. The rocks have been buckled into folds known as anticlines and synclines.

Foundations of the Landscape - Formation of the Rocks

The Glen Roy hills today represent the eroded remnants of the great Caledonian Mountain Belt that stretched from Scandinavia through Scotland to eastern North America at a time before the Atlantic Ocean had formed

The making of Glen Roy began in Precambrian times (some 1000 million years ago) when sandy and muddy sediments were deposited in shallow water at the margins of an ancient continent to the northwest. In the older parts of these sediments (the Grampian Group), some of the sandstone beds record the effects of storms, and pebbles in a few of the muddy beds may have been dropped from icebergs. Later, there was an increase in the amount of muddy sediments and of lime-rich muds and limestones, which now form a younger suite of rocks (the Appin Group). Precambrian sedimentary rocks up to several kilometres in thickness are preserved in Glen Roy, but undoubtedly they were at one time overlain by many kilometres more of rock which has since been removed by erosion.

Between about 750 and 400 million years ago the Precambrian sediments of the Highlands were involved in the formation of the Caledonian Mountain Belt, a chain of mountains extending through Scotland from Scandinavia to eastern North America. The rocks of the Glen Roy area were probably buried about 10 kilometres deep, in the roots of the mountain belt, where they were subjected to intense compression at temperatures over 600^{0}C. The result was complex folding and the 'cooking' (metamorphism) of the rocks; the sandstones recrystallised and became tougher, the limestones became crystalline marbles and the constituents of the mudstones reacted together to form mica schists, sometimes with garnet (a semi-precious mineral).

Molten material (forming 'igneous rocks') was injected towards the end of the period of folding and metamorphism. It formed bodies of grey and pink granite, pegmatite veins with large crystals of quartz and feldspar, and dark green basic rock (appinite) characterised by well-formed crystals of the mineral hornblende. Later, in early Devonian times, about 400 million years ago, dark grey igneous dykes were intruded into the Glen Roy area. These were associated with a volcano which developed where Ben Nevis is now situated.

By this time the Caledonian mountain chain had been much reduced by erosion, and movement was taking place on the Great Glen Fault, a major line of weakness in the Earth's crust. A narrow basin or valley developed there and fans of gravel and sand were deposited in the basin by streams flowing from the highlands on either side; the gravels and sands consolidated to form the Devonian conglomerates and sandstones that occur today along parts of the Great Glen.

The Ice Age – Glaciers Shape the Landscape

View of Glen Roy showing the form of the glaciated valley

Following the Devonian, there is a gap of nearly 400 million years in the geological record of Glen Roy. By the end of the Neogene, about 2.4 million years ago, the Devonian sandstones and the older metamorphic rocks and granites had been reduced by the action of the sea, and particularly by weathering, landslipping and erosion by rivers, to form rolling countryside not unlike that at present, with some rivers flowing northeastwards and others crossing the line of the present Great Glen in an easterly direction.

About 2.4 million years ago, there was a general cooling of the climate, and another agent in the sculpting of the landscape appeared in the form of glacier ice. At first, the periods of extreme cold were comparatively short, perhaps only 40,000 years or so, and the glaciers were probably confined to the mountains. However, over the last 450,000 years there have been at least four major, intensely cold episodes, during which Scotland was covered by an ice sheet for long periods.

Roche moutonnée in Glen Nevis. A former glacier flowing from right to left has eroded this whaleback-shaped, rocky outcrop. The up-glacier surface (right) has been polished by glacial abrasion, by the grinding action of debris carried at the base of a glacier, whereas fractured rock has been plucked from the down-glacier side (left)

The glaciers and ice sheets removed all the pre-glacial soil and other soft superficial deposits, and excavated steep-sided, flat-bottomed glens, of which Glen Roy and the Great Glen are good examples. On a smaller scale, the erosive power of the carpet of rock debris transported at the base of the ice is apparent from the rocky outcrops that have been smoothed off to form the scratched (striated) and polished rock surfaces of 'whalebacks' and 'roches moutonnées'; the action was like that of a very coarse sandpaper. Some particularly good examples can be seen in Glen Nevis.

In geological terms this brings us almost up to the present day. We are still technically living in the Ice Age (major ice sheets remain over Greenland and Antarctica), but in a warmer, so-called 'interglacial' interval. The last time an ice sheet covered the whole of Scotland was less than 20,000 years ago during the Late Devensian glaciation. Following its disappearance during a warmer interval, glaciers again entered the Glen Roy area during the brief, but very cold period of the Loch Lomond Stadial, which is thought to have begun about 12,900 years ago. The glaciers may have persisted until about 11,500 years ago, a time when settled communities were already flourishing in the Middle East. It is this period that is critical to our understanding of how the Parallel Roads were formed.

Moreno Glacier, Argentina

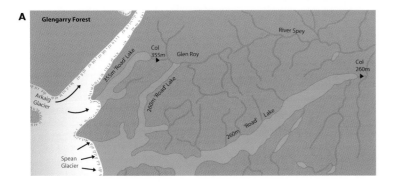

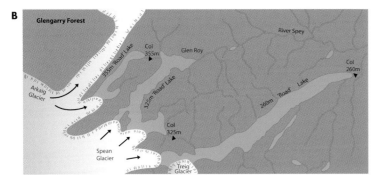

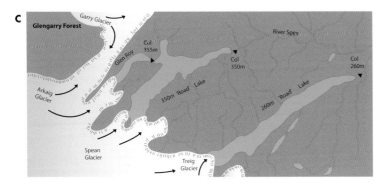

An icefield developed to the west of Glen Roy and the Great Glen during the Loch Lomond Stadial, with a further ice centre to the south, over Rannoch Moor. Glaciers flowed eastwards along the glens from the icefield in the Western Highlands. One tongue of ice blocked the entrance to Glen Gloy, while another extended eastwards to block lower Glen Roy. Here it met a glacier that had extended into the middle section of Glen Spean from the Loch Treig valley. The blocking of Glen Spean led to a lake being impounded with a surface level of about 260 metres above sea level. This lake overflowed eastwards through the Loch Laggan valley, to drain eventually into the River Spey (Diagram **A**). As the glacier advanced up lower Glen Roy, it cut off a lake in this valley and the rising water eventually found its way across a pass at 325 metres above sea level (Diagram **B**).

A further advance of the glacier up Glen Roy resulted in the blocking of this exit for the water, and the lake rose to 350 metres, to drain across the low ground at the head of the Roy and Spey glens (Diagram **C**). A lake at a level of 355 metres above sea level impounded in Glen Gloy drained through the head of this glen across a pass into Glen Roy. As the ice retreated, the overflows were unblocked in the reverse order; finally the ice dam broke near Spean Bridge and the 260 metres lake drained away under the glacier very suddenly and rapidly towards the Great Glen. The sequence of diagrams shows the progressive advance of glaciers into Glen Roy and adjacent glens, producing ice-dammed lakes at successively higher levels of **A** 260 metres above sea level; **B** 325 metres above sea level; and **C** 350 metres above sea level.

An aerial view of the three parallel roads cut into
the hillside on the west side of Glen Roy

The Parallel Roads represent the shorelines of the ice-dammed lakes. Typically they are narrow benches (several metres wide) cut into the bedrock of the hillsides and in places covered by remnants of lake beach gravel. They extend along much of Glen Roy and Glen Gloy and parts of Glen Spean. Probably they formed through a combination of intense frost weathering and wave action along the lake shore zone. The control of lake levels by the different cols allowed the lakes to persist for sufficiently long periods such that even the hard, Precambrian bedrock was broken up and eroded.

A view along the 325 metres Parallel Road in Glen Roy showing the shoreline cut into the hillside

Later Lake Drainage

As the climate improved about 11,500 years ago, the glacier damming the lakes retreated and the lakes drained by glacier bursts (see explanation on page 15). Effectively, the buoyancy of the water floated the glacier tongue off its bed. This happened suddenly, allowing the lake waters to drain in great floods under the ice. The biggest glacier burst took place after the ice dam had retreated to Spean Bridge, and the lake was at the level of the 260 metres Parallel Road; at this stage some 5 cubic kilometres of water are believed to have escaped under the ice to Loch Ness and into the sea at Inverness. As the ice surface declined, lower lakes were dammed; these also seem to have drained by glacier bursts directed either northeastwards to Loch Ness or southwestwards to Fort William.

The glacier burst that drained the 260 metres lake seems to have taken place under the ice along the Spean Gorge. Some of the later, smaller glacier bursts were directed underneath the ice into the gorge of the River Lundy. Most of the later lakes were probably short-lived, but one at 113 metres above sea level formed a locally-preserved shoreline and was probably longer lived.

Modern Glacial Lakes

Modern glacial lake, Moreno Glacier, Argentina

In modern glacial environments we can find equivalents of the glacial lakes that formed in Glen Roy and neighbouring glens, for example the Märjelensee at the side of the great Aletsch Glacier in Switzerland and lakes alongside the margins of glaciers in Greenland, Iceland and the Patagonian icefields in South America. These modern equivalents help us to understand the formation and drainage of the Parallel Roads lakes.

A marginal lake, formed where a stream from a side valley is dammed by a glacier, is unstable. This is partly because cracks in the ice are continually opening and closing as the glacier slowly moves down its valley, allowing leakage to take place. Moreover, because ice is less dense than water, once the lake reaches a certain size the ice tends to float, allowing water to discharge, under or alongside the glacier, sometimes within a few hours.

This very rapid drainage is known as a glacier burst or by the Icelandic term, 'jökulhlaup'. However, where water from the lake is able to escape over a low barrier into another valley, this acts as a control on its level, and discharge under or along the margin of the glacier is less likely.

Legacy of the Ice - Moraines

A moraine ridge near the Commando Memorial north-west of Spean Bridge. The ridge crosses the photo diagonally from lower left to middle right

The material deposited at the base of a glacier (till or boulder clay) often consists of a compact mixture of muddy sand, gravel and boulders. Many of the stones are scratched

Rock fragments, sand and clay eroded and picked up from the ground beneath a glacier are carried forward as a carpet of debris at the base of the ice. Some of this material (till or boulder clay) is deposited as a layer beneath the glacier (till sheet), but some is transported to the glacier edge where it accumulates as mounds or ridges (moraines). Large moraines are formed at times when the ice front remains in the same place for lengthy periods. They are, therefore, good indicators of the position of a former ice front. In many places in Scotland, well-formed terminal moraines mark the maximum extent of the glaciers of the last really cold episode, the Loch Lomond Stadial.

A series of large terminal moraines at the west end of Loch Laggan near the Laggan Dam marks the final position of a powerful glacier that moved out of the Loch Treig glen and merged with the glacier in Glen Spean. The moraines here are formed chiefly of boulders and gravel. West of Spean Bridge, low moraine ridges occur near Brackletter and Leanachan. These are believed to mark the position of the retreating Spean glacier and to have formed beneath the lake waters.

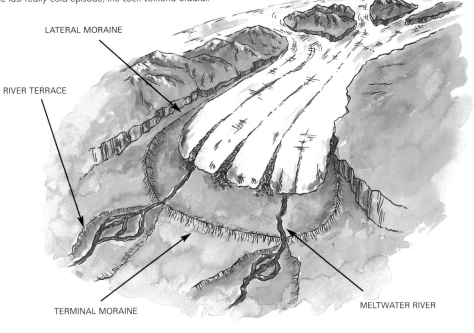

LATERAL MORAINE

RIVER TERRACE

TERMINAL MORAINE

MELTWATER RIVER

Schematic representation of landforms formed at a valley glacier margin

Legacy of Water - Deposits of Lakes and Rivers

The fan at Brunachan was formed by deposition of sands and gravels from a powerful stream coming from a side valley into Glen Roy

As the glaciers melted away during the end of the last very cold period, the deposits they left behind were readily eroded by rivers. Gravel and sand were carried by streams and redeposited as fans where the streams entered larger glens; particularly good examples can be seen on the east side of Glen Roy at Brunachan and the Allt Reinich. Where the rivers entered lakes, deltas were formed as their sediment loads were dropped suddenly in the standing water. At Fersit, a delta was built out across buried ice which later melted, causing collapse of the sediments and the formation of large depressions called kettle holes (see photo p26). When the Parallel Road lakes were in existence, mud carried into them settled out as layers of silt and clay on the floor of Glen Roy, Glen Gloy and Glen Spean. Such laminated silt and clay can be seen today in road cuttings, for instance along the public road in Glen Roy. As their discharges and sediment supply varied, the rivers at different times built up thick deposits of sand and gravels on the floors of the glens, or incised down into these deposits forming extensive suites of river terraces, for example between Roy Bridge and Spean Bridge in Glen Spean.

18

A massive accumulation of bedded sand and gravel was formed by glacial meltwaters draining a glacier in Glen Turret

Folded lake silts in Glen Roy. Silts deposited in glacial lakes are often unstable. Any shock, such as that caused by a landslide or earthquake can cause the upper layers in the silt to buckle and fold

An Unstable Landscape

Glacial erosion produced steep-sided glens, some of which are unstable. In some cases the result is slow, deep downhill creep of the rocks. In others, the instability results in landslips. When the Parallel Road lakes drained, a great weight of water was removed very quickly from the glen sides, causing them to be particularly unstable and prone to landslipping. Landslips formed in this way are well displayed in Glen Roy, for example near Braeroy. Catastrophic emptying of modern reservoirs is known to be accompanied by small earthquakes, and it is probable that there were quakes as the Parallel Road lakes were drained.

Although the hill slopes are now mostly stable, the public road in Glen Roy needs to be repaired from time to time in response to local slips, washouts and debris flows. Modern river erosion is also locally active in undercutting older river terraces.

The sheets of muddy debris, sand and gravel left behind as the ice melted away continue to be eroded, as is clear from the spectacular river cliffs that dissect a large outwash fan near Braeroy, and by the ever shifting course of the river nearby.

Water accumulating after heavy rain in the winter of 1989-1990 burst through the old landslip opposite Brunachan in Glen Roy, causing a debris flow of mud and gravel that carried away the road. An observer described the material as "flowing like porridge" for over an hour

Interpreting the Landscape - Changing Times and Ideas

Right: Charles Darwin. Best known for his theory of evolution, he believed that the Parallel Roads were former sea margins, but later changed his mind and accepted that they were lake shorelines

Left: Louis Agassiz. An expert on fossil fish, he became interested in Alpine glaciers and proposed that much of Northern Europe, including the British Isles, had once been covered by a vast ice sheet like that in Greenland or Antarctica today. Agassiz visited Glen Roy in 1840. What he saw there helped to confirm his ideas about the glacier theory

Above: Thomas Jamieson, from Ellon, suggested that glaciers came and went in Scotland several times during the Ice Age. He was the first to work out a detailed history of the formation and drainage of Parallel Road lakes

The Parallel Roads provided easy routes for travellers in a region where communication was difficult, long before road building began early in the 18th century. They were attributed variously to the activities of the mythical Gaelic hero-giant Fingal (of Fingal's Cave fame) and to the work of the early Kings of Scotland. Certainly by the late 18th and early 19th centuries the Parallel Roads were one of the sights of Scotland and were being visited by the local gentry such as the Grants of Rothiemurchus, as recorded in 'Memoirs of a Highland Lady'.

The controversy over the formation of the Parallel Roads illustrates the development of science in the light of two 19th century discoveries; that sea-level can rise and fall in response to earth movements and that

glaciers had existed in Scotland in the geologically recent past. The view that the Parallel Roads were old marine shorelines was championed in 1838 by the young Charles Darwin, who, fresh from his voyage to South America, had been deeply impressed by the uplift of the Chilean seashore by recent earthquakes. The originally less popular view, that the Roads were lake shorelines, came to prominence very shortly afterwards following the visit to Scotland of the Swiss geologist Louis Agassiz in 1840. Agassiz suggested a key mechanism for the otherwise puzzling formation of lakes in these glens, damming by glacier ice; this was put on a firm footing by Thomas Jamieson some 20 years later. The interest in the Parallel Roads extended to government circles, and the Ordnance Survey diverted some of its effort into specially surveying the Parallel Roads, showing that they were indeed (almost) horizontal and could be lake shorelines.

Historically, also, the landforms in Glen Roy and Glen Spean, near Loch Treig, played a key part in convincing Agassiz of the reality of the former existence of glaciers in Scotland. They provided crucial field evidence that he needed to confirm the theory of a great ice age. Following his visit, he sent a now famous letter from Fort Augustus, announcing publically the glacial theory. This world exclusive appeared in The Scotsman on 7th October 1840.

The Parallel Roads –
An Area of International Importance for Earth Heritage

A massive outwash fan of sand and gravel (see photo p19 top) fills the entrance to Glen Turrett. The fan was deposited in front of a glacier in the upper part of the glen before the formation of the 325 and 350 metres Parallel Roads (seen on the hillside right of centre). The front of the fan has been truncated by later river erosion

The landforms and deposits in Glen Roy, Glen Gloy and Glen Spean are an internationally important part of Scotland's Earth heritage. They provide the clearest evidence in Britain for the formation and catastrophic drainage of a series of ice dammed lakes at the end of the last glaciation. The features were first recognised over 150 years ago, and have subsequently appeared as classic examples in many textbooks.

The Parallel Roads are exceptional in terms of the extent, clarity and degree of development of the glacial lake shorelines, as well as for the range of associated landforms and deposits preserved in a relatively compact area. These record in detail the processes of landscape development both during and following successive stages of glacial lake development and catastrophic drainage.

The Parallel Roads and associated landforms are protected as a Site of Special Scientific Interest (SSSI). Part of Glen Roy is also a National Nature Reserve. The principal pressures on the Earth heritage of the area are from blanket afforestation which hides the landforms, and quarrying for sand and gravel which destroys them. Other activities such as building or construction of roads and tracks can have a locally damaging impact which can be cumulative over time.

The Parallel Roads and a large, dissected alluvial fan at Coire na Reinich in Glen Roy

Localities of Particular Interest

View down the parallel roads

The Parallel Roads and associated landforms can be seen at many localities in Glen Roy, Glen Gloy and Glen Spean. Among the best are:

1. the view of the Parallel Roads from the viewpoint on the public road in Glen Roy;

2. the views of the alluvial fans at Brunnachan and Allt na Reinich from the public road in Glen Roy;

3. the outwash fan in Glen Turret with lateral moraines along the north-east side of the glen;

4. the river terraces in upper Glen Roy between Braeroy and Burn of Agie;

5. the landslip at Braeroy;

6. the deltas and end moraine and lateral moraines at Roughburn, near the Laggan dam;

7. the delta with kettle holes at Fersit, near Loch Treig

8. the river terraces between Roy Bridge and Spean Bridge;

9. the lake deposits (silts) at many localities by the roadside in Glen Roy.

10. lateral moraines north of Laggan Dam

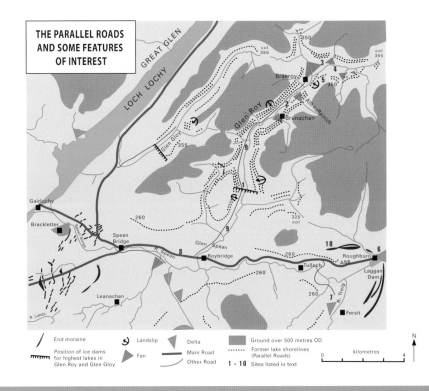

THE PARALLEL ROADS AND SOME FEATURES OF INTEREST

End moraine	Landslip	Delta
Position of ice dams for highest lakes in Glen Roy and Glen Gloy	Fan	Main Road
		Other Road

Ground over 500 metres OD

Former lake shorelines (Parallel Roads)

1 - 10 Sites listed in text

Deposits of moraine, near Roughburn (locality 6)

The Landscape Today

Today Glen Roy is a place of contrasts. The glen's upper reaches are sparsely wooded with few houses or farms. The people of the tiny villages scattered along the lower glen have grasped the opportunity to farm the more fertile soil and use the shelter of dappled woodland straddling the burnsides. The bright green grazed fields at the mouth of the glen contrast with the subtle mosaic of wetland heath, unimproved grassland and bracken that clothe the more remote and rugged slopes at its head.

The journey along Glen Roy begins on a single track road winding gently up through a picturesque landscape of pasture and woodland. On rounding a bend, a panorama of open hillsides suddenly opens up, dramatically revealing the three Parallel Roads stretching as far as the eye can see. The 'roads' form perfect contour lines – snaking in and out of the glen's irregular sides but, like tidemarks on a bath, maintaining precisely the same height throughout.

The ancient loch shorelines are made visible by the fall of light on their terraced forms and by subtle changes in vegetation pattern caused by differences in the underlying ground conditions. Such perfectly level lines in nature are unusual and the regularity of the 'roads' is further emphasised by their marked contrast to the organic shapes of the gently rounded hills, undulating ridges and sinuous river course of this rugged landscape.

The peacefulness and lack of development within Glen Roy is largely due to its relative inaccessibility, there being no through road beyond the head of the glen. In contrast, neighbouring Glen Spean has a long history as one of the most accessible east-west links in the Highlands.

Spean Bridge was the main exit from the Great Glen for cattle drovers going south from Skye to the trysts (markets) at Crieff and Falkirk. More recently, the Glasgow to Fort William railway also took advantage of these more accessible passes. Established to capitalise on this well travelled route are inns, hotels and small settlements scattered along the western end of Glen Spean.

Scottish Natural Heritage
and the British Geological Survey

Scottish Natural Heritage is a government body. Its aim is to help people enjoy Scotland's natural heritage responsibly, understand it more fully and use it wisely so that it can be sustained for future generations.

Scottish Natural Heritage
12 Hope Terrace
Edinburgh EH9 2AS

SCOTTISH
NATURAL
HERITAGE

The British Geological Survey maintains up-to-date knowledge of the geology of the UK and its continental shelf. It carries out surveys and geological research.
The Scottish Office of BGS is sited in Edinburgh. The office runs an advisory and information service, a geological library and a well-stocked geological bookshop.

British Geological Survey
Murchison House
West Mains Road
Edinburgh EH9 3LA

**British
Geological Survey**
NATURAL ENVIRONMENT RESEARCH COUNCIL

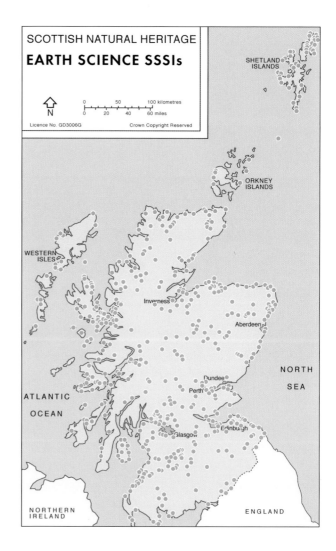

SCOTTISH NATURAL HERITAGE
EARTH SCIENCE SSSIs

N

0   50   100 kilometres
0   20   40   60 miles

Licence No. GD3006G   Crown Copyright Reserved

SHETLAND ISLANDS

ORKNEY ISLANDS

WESTERN ISLES

Inverness

Aberdeen

NORTH SEA

ATLANTIC OCEAN

Dundee
Perth
Glasgow
Edinburgh

NORTHERN IRELAND

ENGLAND

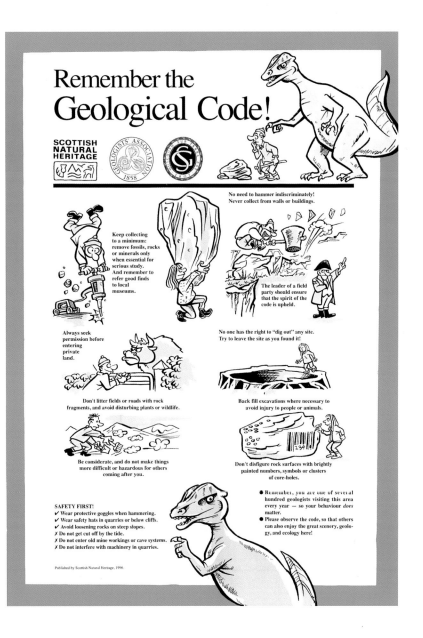

Remember the Geological Code!

SCOTTISH NATURAL HERITAGE

Keep collecting to a minimum: remove fossils, rocks or minerals only when essential for serious study. And remember to refer good finds to local museums.

No need to hammer indiscriminately! Never collect from walls or buildings.

The leader of a field party should ensure that the spirit of the code is upheld.

Always seek permission before entering private land.

No one has the right to "dig out" any site. Try to leave the site as you found it!

Don't litter fields or roads with rock fragments, and avoid disturbing plants or wildlife.

Back fill excavations where necessary to avoid injury to people or animals.

Be considerate, and do not make things more difficult or hazardous for others coming after you.

Don't disfigure rock surfaces with brightly painted numbers, symbols or clusters of core-holes.

SAFETY FIRST!
✔ Wear protective goggles when hammering.
✔ Wear safety hats in quarries or below cliffs.
✔ Avoid loosening rocks on steep slopes.
✗ Do not get cut off by the tide.
✗ Do not enter old mine workings or cave systems.
✗ Do not interfere with machinery in quarries.

● Remember, you are one of several hundred geologists visiting this area every year — so your behaviour *does* matter.
● Please observe the code, so that others can also enjoy the great scenery, geology, and ecology here!

Published by Scottish Natural Heritage, 1996.

Also in the Landscape Fashioned by Geology series...

Arran and the Clyde Islands

The diverse landscapes of Arran and the Clyde Islands mark the boundary between Highland and Lowland. Discover the ancient secrets and the appeal of these well-loved islands.

David McAdam & Steve Robertson
ISBN 1 85397 287 8 pbk 24pp £3.00

Cairngorms

Their broad plateaux, steep sided glens and deep corries make the Cairngorms one of the foremost mountain landscapes in Britain. Discover how they were fashioned by weathering, glaciers and rivers.

John Gordon, Vanessa Brazier,
Rob Threadgold & Sarah Keast
ISBN 1 85397 086 7 pbk 28pp £2.00

East Lothian and the Borders

Underneath the calm facade of south east Scotland's fertile plains and rolling hills lies a complex structure, which reflects an eventful geological history.

David McAdam & Phil Stone
ISBN 1 85397 242 8 pbk 26pp £3.00

Edinburgh and West Lothian

The tranquil appearance of the city of Edinburgh nestling between the surrounding hills and the undulating countryside of West Lothian belies their dramatic volcanic past.

David McAdam
ISBN 1 85397 327 0 pbk 44pp £4.95

Fife and Tayside

The dramatic coastline and volcanic hills of Fife and Tayside are testiment to the dramatic geological past. The story is set at a time when Scotland sat astride the equator.

Mike Browne, Alan McKirdy & David McAdam
ISBN 1 85397 110 3 pbk 36pp £3.95

Loch Lomond to Stirling

The heart of Scotland encompasses some of the most diverse landscapes in Scotland. From the low Carse to the mountain tops - find out how these modern landscapes reflect the geological changes of the past.

Mike Browne & John Mendum
ISBN 1 85397 119 7 pbk 26pp £2.00

Northwest Highlands

Providing an ancient bulwark to Atlantic storms, the stunning scenery we see today in Northwest Highlands was created by the dramatic collision of continents. This book tells a dramatic tale of Scotland's journey through time - our links to Canada, Greenland and Scandinavia and the exploits of the early geological explorers.

John Mendum, Jon Merritt & Alan McKirdy
ISBN 1 85397 139 1 pbk 52pp £6.95

Orkney and Shetland

These northern outposts of Scotland hold a great fascination for the geologist. Starting 3 billion years ago, their story tells of colliding continents, bizarre lifeforms and a landscape which continues to be eroded by the pounding force of the Atlantic.

Clive Auton, Terry Fletcher & David Gould ISBN 1 85397 220 7 pbk 24pp £2.50

Rum and the Small Isles

The silhouette of Rum is one of the most dramatic sights on Scotland's west coast. Its diverse rocks and the landscapes they form have developed over billions of years as this part of the Earth's crust moved across the planet. This guide beautifully illustrates the traces of ancient seas and rivers in the rocks and, more recently, Rum's violent volcanic history as the North Atlantic rifted open.

Kathryn Goodenough & Tom Bradwell   ISBN 1 85397 370 2 pbk 48pp £5.95

Skye

Skye is one of Scotland's most popular tourist destinations, and deservedly so. But what would Skye be without the jagged peaks of the Cuillin or the intriguing rock formations of the Quirang? In many ways it is the geology of Skye that attracts its visitors and this booklet helps you to understand how the mountains, rocks and lochs were formed.

David Stephenson & Jon Merritt   ISBN 1 85397 026 3 pbk 24pp £2.50

Scotland: the creation of its natural landscape

Scotland: the Creation of its Natural Landscape provides a wealth of information on how Scotland was created and the events that took place there through the aeons. But the story doesn't stop back in the mists of time, it continually unfolds and this book provides up to the minute information on geological events taking place beneath our feet. It also provides a history of geological science and highlights the enormous contribution Scots geologists have made to the world.

Alan McKirdy & Roger Crofts   ISBN 1 85397 004 2 pbk 64pp £7.50

Series Editor: Alan McKirdy (SNH)

Other books soon to be produced in the series include:
Glasgow • Mull and Iona

SNH Publication Order Form

Title	Price	Quantity
Arran & the Clyde Islands	£3.00	
Cairngorms	£2.00	
East Lothian & the Borders	£3.00	
Edinburgh & West Lothian	£4.95	
Fife & Tayside	£4.95	
Glen Roy	£4.95	
Loch Lomond to Stirling	£2.00	
Northwest Highlands	£6.95	
Orkney & Shetland	£2.50	
Rum and the Small Isles	£5.95	
Skye	£3.95	
Scotland: the Creation of its natural landscape	£7.50	

Postage and packaging: free of charge within the UK.

A standard charge of £2.95 will be applied to all orders from the EU.

Elsewhere a standard charge of £5.50 will apply.

Please complete in **BLOCK CAPITALS**

Name _____

Address _____

_____

_____

Post Code

Type of Credit Card   **VISA** ☐   EUROCARD MasterCard ☐

Name of card holder _____

Card Number

☐☐☐☐   ☐☐☐☐   ☐☐☐☐   ☐☐☐☐

Expiry Date ☐☐ ☐☐

Send order and cheque made payable to Scottish Natural Heritage to:
Scottish Natural Heritage, Design and Publications, Battleby, Redgorton,
Perth PH1 3EW
E-mail: pubs@redgore.demon.co.uk   www.snh.org.uk

We may want to send you details of other SNH publications, please tick the box below if you do not want this. We will not pass your details to anyone else.

I do not wish to receive information on SNH publications ☐

Please add my name to the mailing list for the   SNH Magazine ☐

Publications Catalogue ☐